GILES

SUNDAY EXPRESS & DAILY EXPRESS
CARTOONS

Twenty-ninth Series

D1513657

A DAILY EXPRESS PUBLICATION

60p

INTRODUCTION

by

TOMMY
COOPER

I think "Giles" is the funniest cartoonist in the world. He makes me, like millions of others, laugh out loud. He appeals to all ages, His dogs and animals have such funny faces, you can see what they are thinking and are almost human.

Many a time I have been travelling in a train, and I start to laugh at the thought of one of his cartoons that morning, and people look at me as if I'm stark raving mad.

They say that a good laugh is a tonic, to me Carl Giles is the greatest tonic ever.

Tommy Cooper

"Daddy was very rude to Teddy. He says Teddy must stop phoning him at the office now the phone charges have gone up again."

Daily Express, July 18th, 1974

"My dad says Cyprus isn't the only holiday resort that's got tyrants."

Daily Express, July 20th, 1974

"The trouble is, madam, if I alter course to avoid trouble from Cyprus we stand a greater risk of being torpedoed by Egypt."

Sunday Express, July 21st, 1974

"I must say one feels far from with it listening to one's pupils discussing where they're taking their children for the hols."

Daily Express, July 23rd, 1974

"As a matter of fact we do not think this is better than taking one of those chancy holidays in the Med."

Sunday Express, July 28th, 1974

"You know how it goes—'If Reg Harris can do it at his age . . .'!"

Daily Express, July 30th, 1974

"We will lift up our eyes unto the heavens so that the member of our flock who hath inadvertently nicked the sugar may return it unseen."

Sunday Express, August 4th, 1974

"Eggs! Super! The galley slave will soon rustle up something for everybody."

Daily Express, August 6th, 1974

"I am NOT streaking in front of the Royal Yacht!"

Daily Express, August 8th, 1974

"Marooning you for putting us aground won't be too bad—you've got non-stop Nixon on the radio for company."

Daily Express, August 10th, 1974

"Inspired by the gorgeous girl golfers at Sunningdale, my wife's determined to challenge male dominance on the links."

Sunday Express, August 11th, 1974

"I know the mini's fini, Honey—and of course your new midi suits you—would Harry tell you it suited you if it didn't, Honey?"

Daily Express, August 15th, 1974

"Protection, mate. First sign of aggro out of any of 'em and pow!!"

Daily Express, August 17th, 1974

"Roughly translated it means as your package tour has folded a spaghetti and chips is one day in the kitchen for her and two days cement mixing for you."

Sunday Express, August 18th, 1974

"He says if Tommy Docherty is speaking up for us what are the Fuzz beefing about?"

Daily Express, August 20th, 1974

"I don't think André liked you asking him what he thought of the Shirley Williams inquiry into the hairdressers' price-fixing game."

Daily Express, August 22nd, 1974

"That was a 42-footer with six Mercruiser 950 h.p. engines."

Daily Express, August 24th, 1974

"My 2 lb. sugar allocation I just signed for—it's gorn!"

Daily Express, August 29th, 1974

"If it's not Jeremy Thorpe trying another stunt who is it?"

Sunday Express, September 1st, 1974

"DON'T YOU DARE."

Daily Express, September 3rd, 1974

"That's what I said to mine: 'You come home here saying you're on strike again—no sex'."

Daily Express, September 5th, 1974

"They thought they'd better tell us—they're holding another pop-festival in Hyde Park, Saturday at 14.00 hrs."

Daily Express, September 7th, 1974

"Now they're banning the under-17s from football we mustn't suppress their inner emotions."

Sunday Express, September 8th, 1974

"A nice hero's welcome from the United Supporters' Club this is!"

Daily Express, September 12th, 1974

"Yes, I did read about the call for the nation to produce more food. Everybody out!"

Daily Express, September 14th, 1974

"Ask him why, if he won the Battle of Britain, are we still short of sugar?"

Sunday Express, September 15th, 1974

"A Mr. Thorpe wants to know if we've got a show-cage for his hamster."

Daily Express, September 17th, 1974

"Two elections this year! I had four stitches in my finger the first time I patted this one's head."

Sunday Express, September 22nd, 1974

"Achtung! One of your 'dedicated men and women' approaching, 'who act as custodians to our general knowledge' according to the Daily Express."

Daily Express, September 24th, 1974

"I have a letter from the Playboy Club informing me there is a shortage of bunny girls, but with a name like Hortense Cholmondeley-Farquharson, perhaps not."

Daily Express, September 26th, 1974

"Now drill another one there, just big enough to poke their toilet rolls through."

Daily Express, September 28th, 1974

"Come off it, Daddy, the promises you've written in your speech can't be as funny as all that."

Sunday Express, September 29th, 1974

"Here we are, Sidney. 'A Japanese scientist says the days are getting shorter because the world is spinning 2,000th of a second of a day faster.' Which works out that you're being overpaid for 83.25 seconds per hour."

Daily Express, October 1st, 1974

"The last one put his coat down and bought me two gins and tonics."

Sunday Express, October 6th, 1974

"Now, if Michelangelo will remove his portraits of our three political leaders with which he has desecrated our walls we will discuss his artistic merits after class."

Daily Express, October 8th, 1974

"You don't appear to be down on the voting register Mr., er, Chia-Chia. How long have you been residing in N.W.1?"

Daily Express, October 10th, 1974

"Don't mention the election. He blames me because I stayed in to watch Porridge and Steptoe instead of going to vote."

Sunday Express, October 13th, 1974

"Didn't you read? Princess Anne's passed her heavy goods vehicle driving test."

Daily Express, October 15th, 1974

"And may I ask what you want seats that recline into a double bed as an optional extra for?"

Daily Express, October 17th, 1974

"I've had a word with the lady, Vicar. She's not collecting for the Church Restoration Fund, she's collecting for Grandma's Day."

Sunday Express, October 20th, 1974

"Dammit! Reading anonymous letters about their love lives is one of the few things I like about this job."

Daily Express, October 24th, 1974

"It's not so much what the British Government might think about the Navy's visit to South Africa—it's what some of their missuses might think."

Sunday Express, October 27th, 1974

"Cholmondeley made a joke. He called over: 'Any of you Oliver Twists like some more?'
And one of 'em called back: 'Yes, please'."

Daily Express, October 29th, 1974

"Did you put a jumping cracker under Mr. Hettlethwaite's car?"

Daily Express, October 31st, 1974

"Dad, there's a man at the door with a petition for the abolition of domestic pets. No there isn't."

Sunday Express, November 3rd, 1974

"They've a pretty strong picket line—the Queen, the Queen Mother, Lord Derby, Peter O'Sullevan, to name but a few."

Daily Express, November 7th, 1974

"My Maisie isn't going to like me taking home one of his flaming calves every week in lieu of my pay increase."

Sunday Express, November 10th, 1974

"SHOW THAT TO LAUGHING BOY."

Daily Express, November 12th, 1974

"Today's the day, folks—
Sportsman and Sportswoman
of the year!"

Daily Express, November 15th, 1974

"Our great economist rides again—uses three gallons to come out here to top up at the old price and they're shut."

Sunday Express, November 17th, 1974

"If you'd read Egon Ronay's report on airport meals, you'd know those little hard things on your X-Ray are not concealed bullets—they're called 'Fresh English garden peas'."

Daily Express, November 19th, 1974

"We have discussed democratically at great length the cutting down of our tea staff, and I fear it was a unanimous decision that Heads Miss Lovejoy stays."

Daily Express, November 28th, 1974

"Excuse me, sir—your pipe is upsetting Veronica."

Daily Express, December 3rd, 1974

"FIFTEEN, PLEASE!"

Daily Express, December 5th, 1974

"What is this I hear about you joining the rest of 'em and refusing to work Sundays?"

Sunday Express, December 8th, 1974

"What d'you mean 'Everyone will laugh at 'em'. May I ask just who the hell's going to see 'em?"

Daily Express, December 12th, 1974

"Now who do you think has come all the way across the country to cheer you up?"

Sunday Express, December 15th, 1974

"More industrial unrest—show him anywhere in the New Testament where it says Kings shouldn't tidy up after the donkey as well as Poor Shepherds."

Daily Express, December 17th, 1974

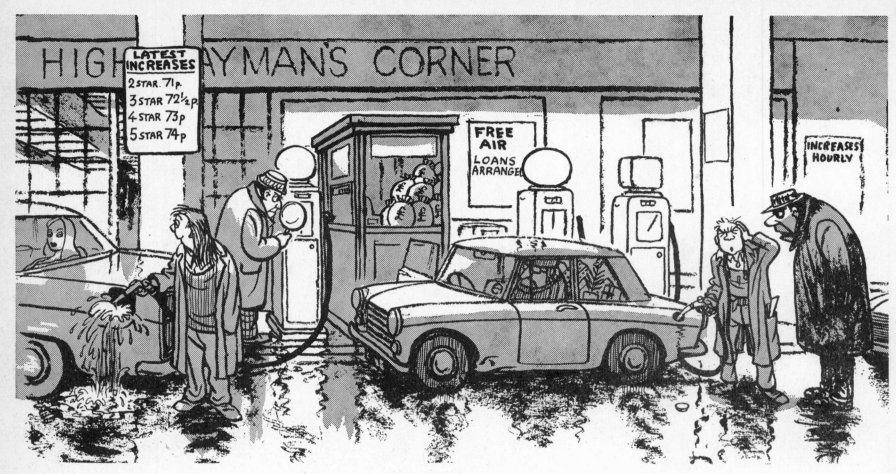

"Don't you Merry Christmas me at 73p a gallon!"

Daily Express, December 19th, 1974

"Timber!"

Sunday Express, December 22nd, 1974

" 'George,' I said, 'Christmas Eve. What better time to ask our new neighbours round for a drink and meet Mummy'."

Daily Express, December 24th, 1974

"Mum! Grandma's gone down behind the piano."

Daily Express, December 28th, 1974

"You never know—some of 'em might come up."

Daily Express, December 31st, 1974

"I don't know what we're going to survive ON in 1975, but I know something I could survive WITHOUT."

Daily Express, January 2nd, 1975

"A Mrs. B. C-A-S-T-L-E.
Toothache."

Daily Express, January 4th, 1975

"You will all be happy to learn that because of the shortage of new teachers Mr. Chalk has volunteered to stay with us for at least another term."

Daily Express, January 7th, 1975

"Funny, it looked much bigger at the Boat Show."

Sunday Express, January 12th, 1975

"If someone had nailed this resolution up with a little more enthusiasm . . ."

Sunday Express, January 19th, 1975

"The calm, unhurried length of time you took to pass me that spanner you should live to be a bleeding 'undred."

Daily Express, January 21st, 1975

"It's their new game—they read about the woman who slammed her door and the house fell down."

Daily Express, January 23rd, 1975

"Margaret, I have performed my social obligations and picked you up, but let there be no misapprehensions about you being my mate."

Daily Express, January 28th, 1975

"As usual, the one who's doing the most hollering is the one who's never put a penny in the TV licence box in her life."

Daily Express, January 31st, 1975

"Here comes Steve McQueen—flitted across the screen for ten seconds in AKENFIELD."

Sunday Express, February 2nd, 1975

"The Supreme Champion of this house has just eaten one of Auntie Ivy's shoes."

Sunday Express, February 9th, 1975

"A hundred-odd Cupid paratroopers tucked up in bed with their wives except mine!"

Sunday Express, February 16th, 1975

"Now they've cancelled the strike it's a pity you fired your driver and sold the horse."

Daily Express, February 18th, 1975

"What do you mean she couldn't do worse than going on the Jimmy Young Prog? She could appear on TV making gravy with Mrs. Tony Blackburn."

Daily Express, February 21st, 1975

"Carol—suppose we ask your daddy to stop calling me Kojak?"

Sunday Express, February 23rd, 1975

"Has she gone?"

Daily Express, February 28th, 1975

"Mum, you know the new extension Dad's building himself to save massive builder's bills?"

Sunday Express, March 2nd, 1975

"In the fever and excitement of yesterday's F.A. quarter finals, I hope you all remembered the Mother's Day flowers."

Sunday Express, March 9th, 1975

"Asking them if they've tried the Foreign Legion doesn't constitute the much-needed encouragement we are supposed to offer them, Miss Rambler."

Daily Express, March 11th, 1975

"Grandma says she could have written a better strip than this when she was eight."

Daily Express, March 14th, 1975

"The Lord introduces British Summer Time in his usual mysterious way, belting with rain out of one window and two inches of snow out of the other."

Sunday Express, March 16th, 1975

"Nurse! I've got one of yer starving paying patients nicking me bickies!"

Daily Express, March 21st, 1975

"Don't worry about my mum and dad for the rehearsal, Tracey—I'll do something about them for your wedding next week."

Sunday Express, March 23rd, 1975

"Captain Hornblower does it again—'No traffic on the East Coast this time of the year, we'll hire a little boat and sail up as far as Grimsby . . .' "

Daily Express, March 25th, 1975

SEASONAL GREETINGS

Daily Express, March 29th, 1975

"Nothing's going to stop him giving the lawn its Easter hair cut with his new mower."

Sunday Express, March 30th, 1975

"I've made a mental note for Whitsun of all the ones who snowballed me at Easter."

Daily Express, April 1st, 1975

"I hope her long-haired banjo-playing git who told me Red Rum couldn't lose won't be honouring us with his presence today."

Sunday Express, April 6th, 1975

"Ring the sales manager and ask why there is a sudden demand for our products in the Manchester area."

Daily Express, April 8th, 1975

"Sign please—'I do solemnly swear when I come down we will not have Denis Healey for breakfast'."

Sunday Express, April 13th, 1975

"I think all this is grossly exaggerated, don't you, dear?"

Daily Express, April 18th, 1975

"Bang goes the first instalment of your new bonus, Doc."

Sunday Express, April 20th, 1975

"That's the bail for your son, Madam, now what about the bail for your husband?"

Daily Express, April 22nd, 1975

"Doctor, you know you were saying how happy you are—all this extra money and fewer patients because the sun is shining?"

Daily Express, April 25th, 1975

"Before you go off to your last match of the season—take a look at where you'll be getting rid of yours for the next few months, Georgie boy."

Sunday Express, April 27th, 1975

"Judging by your Bonny Prince Charlie's waistline, food must be cheaper in Canada."

Daily Express, April 29th, 1975

"While I think of it, your Missus is waiting to hear how you got on after you'd lobbied your M.P."

Daily Express, May 2nd, 1975

"—Will inscrutable Geisha who has half-inched Her Honourable Majesty's other shoe for souvenir please return."

Daily Express, May 8th, 1975

"Here he come agin—'How come they're launching Mr. Heath's new boat today when I ordered mine in 1972 and it's only half started?'"

Daily Express, May 10th, 1975

"Go ye forth and speed the gospel to our flocks and at all times keep your eye on the Fuzz."

(The Bishop of Norwich ordered a fleet of Mopeds for the Vicars of his diocese.)

Sunday Express, May 11th, 1975

"On your feet, corporal—I'm sure His Royal Highness only gave you a karate chop for fun."

Daily Express, May 13th, 1975

"Would our financial resources stand a withdrawal of a few francs for Ronnie to go to la loo?"

Daily Express, May 15th, 1975

"Tell Carol ol' blue eyes is here."

Daily Express, May 17th, 1975

"I'm not walking off as a protest against the umpire's decision—I'm walking off because I hate the damn game and I'm frozen stiff."

Sunday Express, May 18th, 1975

"Psst!"

Daily Express, May 24th, 1975

"Is that you, Minister? Could you please come over and exorcise my wee Scottie? He's full of wee devils since he heard Scotland lost."

Sunday Express, May 25th, 1975

"I'll tell you what I think about Bank Holidays by the sea."

Daily Express, May 27th, 1975

"His Royal Highness busting Queen's Regulations is one thing—Ordinary Seaman Jones busting 'em is another. GIT IT ORF!"

Daily Express, May 30th, 1975

"My Dad's dressed like that so you don't think he comes from Leeds."

Daily Express, May 31st, 1975

"I've fell in this ditch every Saturday night for over twenty years—now he's gorn Bolshie he won't pull me out."

Sunday Express, June 1st, 1975

"Somehow our Referendum Voters section seems to lack the enthusiasm of our Bay City Rollers section."

Daily Express, June 3rd, 1975

"Of *course*, he realises we went to the poll for *his* future, *his* generation, *his* security, don't you, my little sweetheart?"

Daily Express, June 6th, 1975

"Oh dear, Rodney is expounding his theory that now we're the United States of Europe all the blighters should learn to speak English."

Sunday Express, June 8th, 1975

"Here's an amusing little story—'Experts say gripe water has twice the alcohol content of beer . . .'"

Daily Express, June 10th, 1975

"That's how the Aussies do it—bowl 'em on the feet, make 'em hop out of their crease, and BINGO!!"

Daily Express, June 13th, 1975

"Morning, Sir. How about starting the week with being in charge of an offensive weapon, parked in a No Waiting area?"

Daily Express, June 17th, 1975

"When you have finished your splendid impersonation of the Australian bowlers . . ."

Sunday Express, June 22nd, 1975

"There goes my 7 to 4 bet—according to that tic-tac man one of the players has belted a linesman before the game's started."

Daily Express, June 24th, 1975

"Can you borrow a couple of safety-pins for WHAT?"

Daily Express, June 27th, 1975

"I know as a miners' M.P. I've got to do everything Mr. Scargill tells me but I'm damn sure it doesn't include looking after your kids and doing your wife's shopping."

Daily Express, June 29th, 1975

"I must say a Reverend 36-24-36 wouldn't be a bad idea, eh Harry?"

Sunday Express, July 6th, 1975

"Easy on the house-keeping, lass—we haven't got it yet."

Daily Express, July 8th, 1975